CU00404847

VOLUME 3

# SING WITH THE
# Pop
# Standards

**VOLUME 3**

# SING WITH THE CHOIR
# Pop Standards

This publication is not authorised for sale in the United States of America and/or Canada.

Hal Leonard Europe
Distributed by Music Sales

Exclusive Distributors:
Music Sales Limited
14–15 Berners Street, London W1T 3LJ, UK.

Order No. HLE90003837
ISBN 978-1-84938-042-3
This book © Copyright 2009 Hal Leonard Europe

Unauthorised reproduction of any part of this publication by any means
including photocopying is an infringement of copyright.

Cover design by Chloë Alexander
Printed in the USA

**Your Guarantee of Quality**

As publishers, we strive to produce every book to the highest
commercial standards.
The book has been carefully designed to minimise awkward page turns
and to make playing from it a real pleasure.
Throughout, the printing and binding have been planned to ensure a
sturdy, attractive publication which should give years of enjoyment.
If your copy fails to meet our high standards, please inform us and we
will gladly replace it.

www.musicsales.com

# Can't Help Falling In Love

Arranged by
**MARK BRYMER**

Words and Music by **GEORGE DAVID WEISS,
HUGO PERETTI** and **LUIGI CREATORE**

Copyright © 1961; Renewed 1989 Gladys Music (ASCAP)
This arrangement Copyright © 1999 Gladys Music (ASCAP)
Worldwide Rights for Gladys Music Administered by Cherry Lane Music Publishing Company, Inc.
International Copyright Secured   All Rights Reserved

# Let It Be

**Arranged by
KIRBY SHAW**

**Words and Music by JOHN LENNON
and PAUL McCARTNEY**

Copyright © 1970 Sony/ATV Music Publishing LLC
Copyright Renewed
This arrangement Copyright © 1997 Sony/ATV Music Publishing LLC
All Rights Administered by Sony/ATV Music Publishing LLC, 8 Music Square West, Nashville, TN 37203
International Copyright Secured   All Rights Reserved

There will be ___ an an - swer, let it be, ___ let ___ it be. Let it be, ___

___ let it be, ___ let ___ it be, ___ let it be. ___

There will be ___ an an - swer, ___ there will be ___ an an - swer, ___

**Suddenly slow**

*mf Solo*

there will be ___ an an - swer, let it

Oo. ___

# Georgia On My Mind

Arranged by
KIRBY SHAW

Words by STUART GORRELL
Music by HOAGY CARMICHAEL

Copyright © 1930 by Peermusic III, Ltd.
Copyright Renewed
This arrangement Copyright ©1982 by Peermusic III, Ltd.
International Copyright Secured    All Rights Reserved

old____ sweet__ song____ keeps____ Geor-gia on____ my mind.

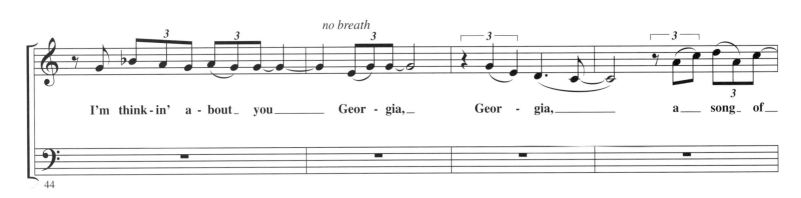

I'm think-in' a-bout_ you_____ Geor - gia,____ Geor - gia,_____ a___ song_ of__

___ you_____ comes as sweet and clear___ as moon-light___ through the___

___ pines._____ Play it for me Geor - gia. Oth - er arms_____

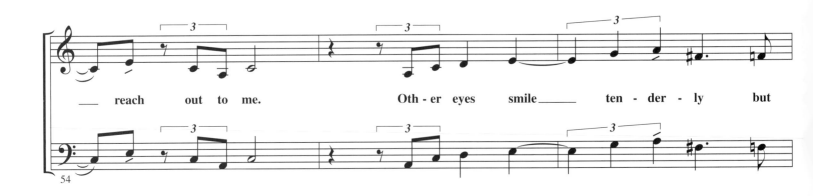

___ reach out to me. Oth - er eyes smile_____ ten - der - ly but

# My Prayer

Arranged by
ED LOJESKI

Music by GEORGES BOULANGER
Lyric and Musical Adaptation by JIMMY KENNEDY

Copyright © 1939 The World Wide Music Co., Ltd., London, England
Copyright Renewed and Assigned to Skidmore Music Co., Inc., New York for U.S.A. and Canada
This arrangement Copyright © 2000 Skidmore Music Co., Inc., New York for U.S.A. and Canada
International Copyright Secured   All Rights Reserved
Used by Permission

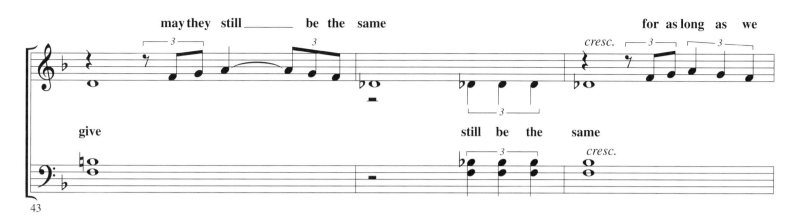

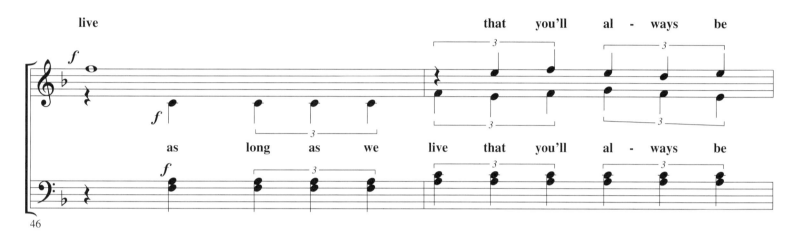

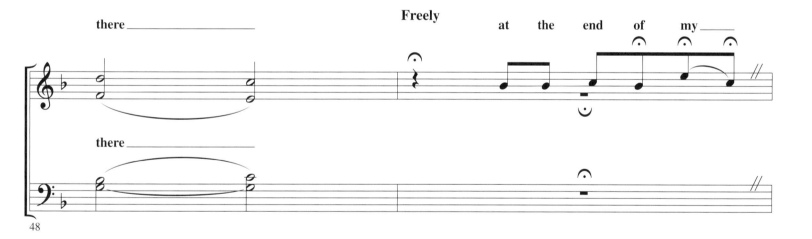

# Skylark

**Arranged by**
**MAC HUFF**

**Words by JOHNNY MERCER**
**Music by HOAGY CARMICHAEL**

Copyright © 1941, 1942 by Songs Of Peer, Ltd. and WB Music Corp.
Copyright Renewed
This arrangement Copyright © 2002 by Songs Of Peer, Ltd. and WB Music Corp.
International Copyright Secured   All Rights Reserved

# Unchained Melody

Arranged by
**MARK BRYMER**

Lyric by HY ZARET
Music by ALEX NORTH

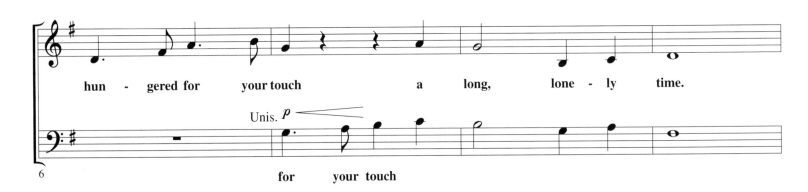

© 1955 (Renewed) FRANK MUSIC CORP.
This arrangement © 1990 FRANK MUSIC CORP.
All Rights Reserved

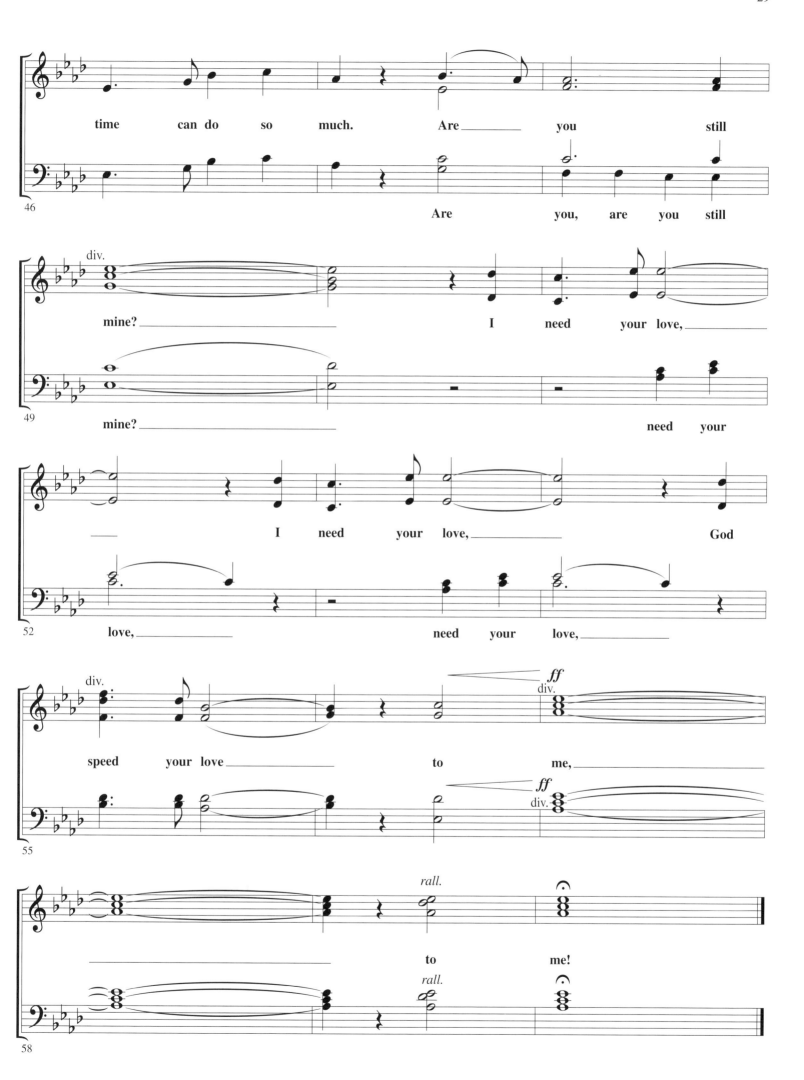

# Yesterday Once More

Arranged by
ED LOJESKI

Words and Music by JOHN BETTIS
and RICHARD CARPENTER

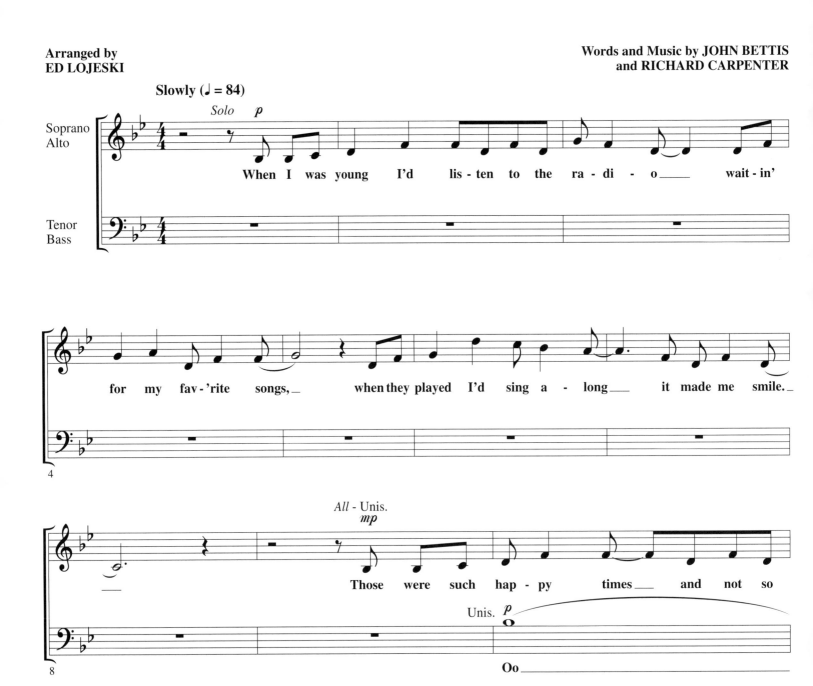

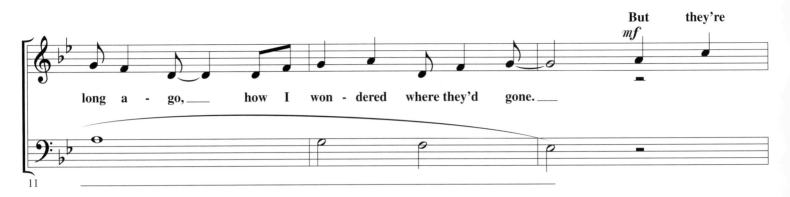

Copyright © 1973 ALMO MUSIC CORP. and HAMMER AND NAILS MUSIC
Copyright Renewed
This arrangement Copyright © 2001 ALMO MUSIC CORP. and HAMMER AND NAILS MUSIC
All Rights Administered by ALMO MUSIC CORP.
All Rights Reserved   Used by Permission

# What A Wonderful World

Arranged by
**MARK BRYMER**

Words and Music by **GEORGE DAVID WEISS**
and **BOB THIELE**

Copyright © 1967 by Range Road Music Inc., Quartet Music and Abilene Music, Inc.
Copyright Renewed
This arrangement Copyright © 1988 by Range Road Music Inc., Quartet Music and Abilene Music, Inc.
International Copyright Secured   All Rights Reserved
Used by Permission